# Contents

This book belongs to:

_____

Oh yes,
Mama.

I'm a little teapot,
**short** and **stout**...

All right, all right. Let's go now.

Say, "Good morning before you begin. Everyone will be looking at you.

I'm a little teapot,
Short and stout,
Here is my handle
And here is my spout ...

# Pepper
## goes to the doctor

Oh dear! That's a bad cold.

Come along,
Pepper.

Aa-a-choo!

Pepper has a bad cold. I'll have a look.

Mama, the doctor forgot to give me an injection!

Pepper, the doctor gives an injectic
only if you really need it. It hurts a
little, but it helps to get well quickly.

The doctor gave me
chocolates. He's nice.

And he has so many toys to play with.

Now have your medicine.

# Pepper
## in the dark

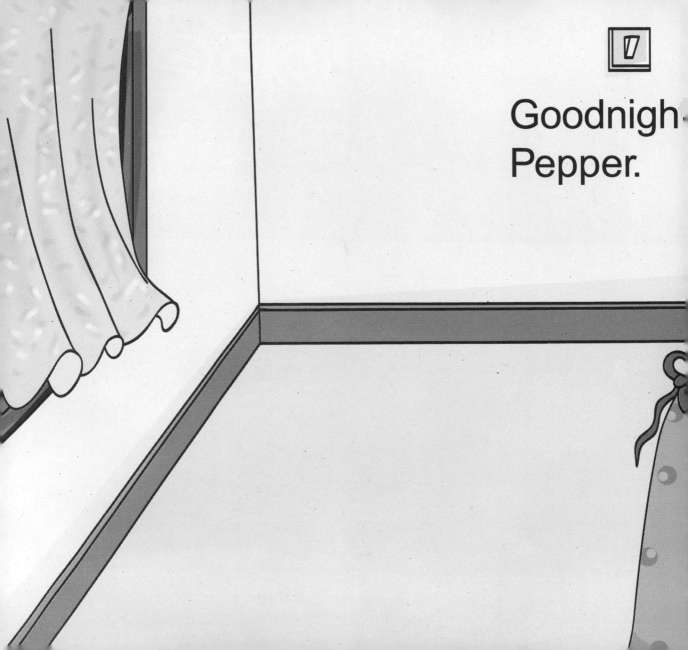

Goodnigh
Pepper.

Goodnight,
Mama.

What thing?

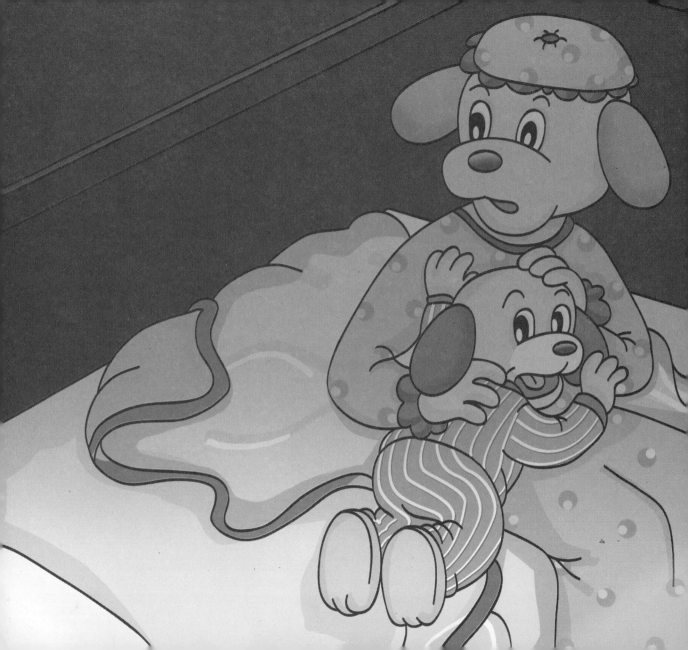

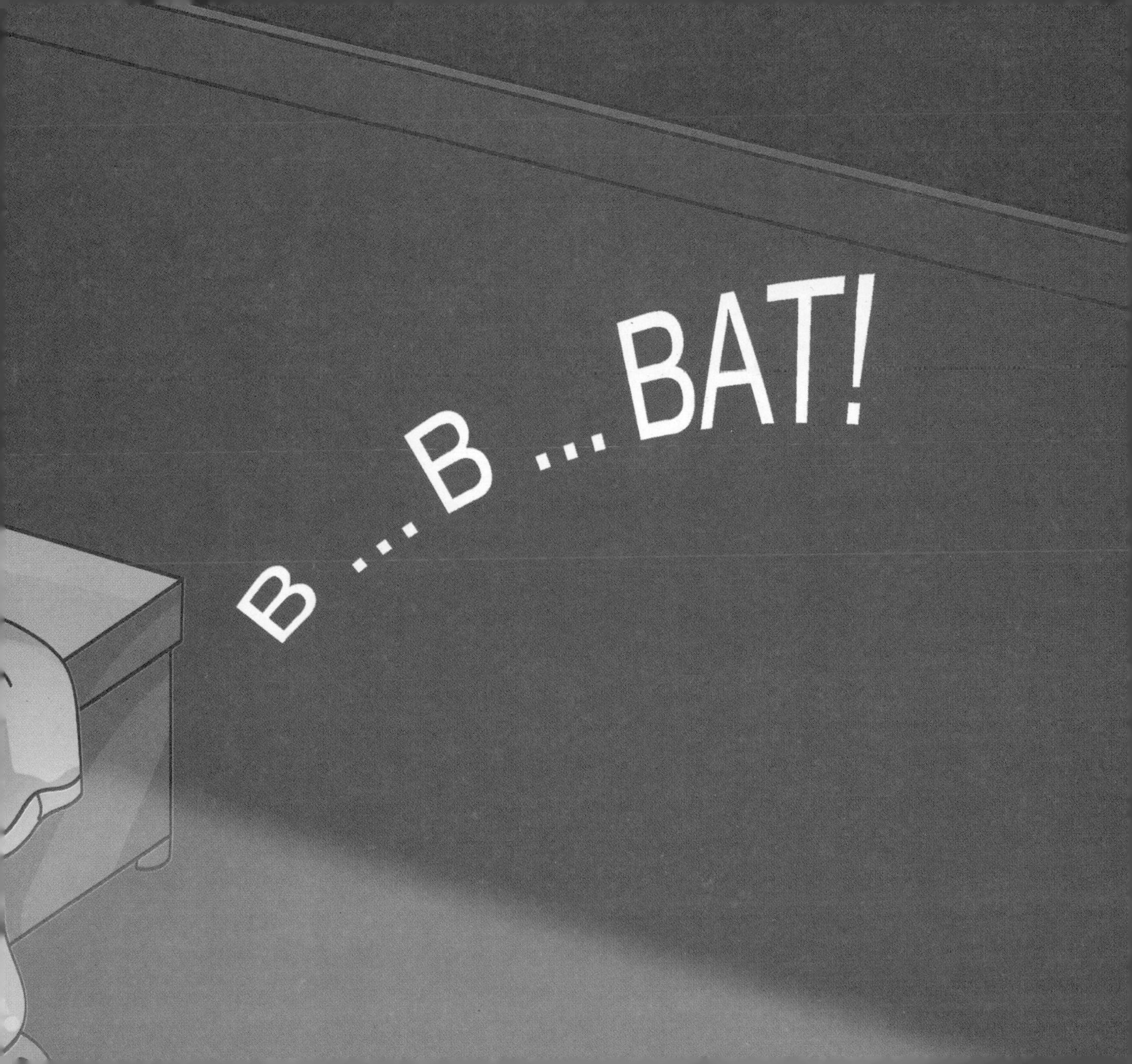
B ... B ... BAT!

A bat? Let's switch
on the light and see

Where's the
bat? Show me.

Huh?

Are you
afraid of
this bat?

I've tied up the curtain. And I'll leave the night light on, OK?

Look, Papa! So many birthday gifts!

Huh? But Mama
said to clear up.

It's called
recycling, Pepper.

No, son. When we re-use something instead of throwing it away, it's called recycling.

So, I can use this paper to wrap Chimp's birthday gift!

But Papa, how will I recycle this can?

Put it in the bin outside. The dump truck will take it to the factory for recycling.

See, we have different bins for different things.

This bin is for
things like
banana peels
and tea leaves
and eggshells.

Ugh! What can we do with those?

We can recycle it into food for the plants in our garden.

That's very good, Pepper!

Can I have the newspaper? I want to make shopping bags for Mama.

WOW! Recycling is fun!

Hey! Don't do that, Chimp.
Someone might slip on
the peel.

Oh, let them. It'll be fun to watch.

# Pepper
## meets his new neighbour

Oh, hi! I'm looking for my ball.

There it is!
I'll get it.

Thanks!

Pepper. I didn't know anyone lived in this house.

Pepper,
come and
play.

This is Polly.
She has just
moved in
here.

Hello, Pepper. I'm Polly's mother. I see you've become friends already.

Bye, Polly, come to play tomorrow.

# POINTS TO PONDER

## 1. Pepper gets stage fright

Your friend trips and falls on the stage. What will you do?

## 2. Pepper goes to the doctor

Who will you go to if you have a toothache?

### 3. Pepper in the dark

What will you do if the lights go off suddenly in your house?

### 4. Pepper learns about recycling

Your mother has come home with many plastic shopping bags. How will you recycle them?